P9-DHK-051

Come Lasses and Lads

NEW ORCHARD EDITIONS
POOLE DORSET

COME Lasses and Lads, get leave of your Dads,

And away to the May-pole hey:

For every he

Has found him a she,

With a Minstrel standing by.

For Willy has found his Jill,
    And Johnny has found his Jone,
To jigg it, jigg it, jigg it, jigg it,
    Jigg it up and down.

R.C

"Strike up," says WATT; "Agreed," says KATE,

"And I prithee, Fiddler, play;"

"Content," says HODGE, and so says MADGE,

For this is a Holiday!

Then every man did take his hat off,

And every girl did curtsey.

"Begin," says HALL; "Ay, ay," says MOLL,
"We'll lead up Packington's pound:"
"No, no," says NOLL, and so says DOLL,
"We'll first go Sellenger's round."

Then every man began
to foot it round about,
And every girl did jet it,
Jet it, jet it in and out.

"You're out," says DICK; "Not I," says NICK,
"The Fiddler played it false;"
"'Tis true," says HUGH, and so says SUE,
And so says nimble ALICE.

The Fiddler then began to play the tune again,
And every girl did trip it,
Trip it, trip it to the men.

"MAID MARIAN!"

Then after an hour, they went to a bower,
And played for ale and cakes,
And kisses too — until they were due
the lasses held the stakes.

R·C

The girls did then begin to quarrel with the men,
And bid them take their kisses back,
and give them their own again,
And bid them take their kisses back
and give them their own again.

Now there they did stay the whole of the day,
And tired the Fiddler quite,
With singing and playing, without any paying,
From morning until night.

R C

They told the Fiddler then,

they'd pay him for his play,

And each a 2-pence, 2-pence, 2-pence,
gave him and went away.

"Good-night," says Harry; "Good-night," says Mary;
"Good-night," says Dolly to John;
"Good-night," says Sue, to her sweetheart Hugh,
"Good-night," says everyone.

Some walked and some did run, Some tarried on the way,
And bound themselves, by kisses twelve, To meet the next Holiday.
And bound themselves, by kisses twelve, To meet the next Holiday.

Link House, West Street, Poole, Dorset BH15 1LL

ISBN 1-85079-110-4

Printed in Portugal by Printer Portugesa